Best Book Reports

Andrea Antico

Troll Associates

Interior Illustrations by: Shirley Beckes

ISBN: 0-8167-2588-8

Printed in the United States of America.

10 9 8 7 6 5 4 3

Contents

Introduction

Best Book Reports will help meet today's challenges in the reading arena. The ideas in this book are entertaining as well as educational, and are designed for all levels of students in grades 2 through 6. Activities range from teacher-directed cooperative-learning experiences to individual exercises that students can work on independently (Activity Sheets). Many pages can be personalized, allowing the student choices and options.

The activities in *Best Book Reports* are practical, innovative, simple ideas that have been used successfully in classrooms, reading centers, and library/media centers. They provide something for every student and teacher; activities will appeal to the artistic student, the creative student, the dramatic student, the quiet reader, the prolific reader, the slow reader, and the nonreader. Many will provoke classroom discussion; others will motivate students to pursue further research and reading. Some involve students' sharing ideas and working cooperatively with one another. The natural combination of reading and writing is a strong element throughout the book. Peer editing plays an active role in many of the activities.

The media that distract children from reading today—movies, television, videos—can be incorporated into many of the book reports described in this book. And in many other ways, these book reports involve activities that are popular even with children who do not read voluntarily. Playing memory games, creating comic strips, making T-shirts, organizing puppet shows, pantomiming, and playing baseball are only a few of the fun and popular activities integrated with reading in this book. When reading becomes a part of the activities that today's children love, they become excited about it and understand that the book report can be an interesting, personal way of sharing books and thoughts with friends, family, and schoolmates.

It is recommended that you browse through the table of contents, skim the book, and then read it thoroughly at your leisure. Check off the activities that have the most appeal to you, jot notes about modifying others to suit your needs, and disregard any that might not work with your particular set of students.

Enjoy *Best Book Reports*. Use it whenever and wherever it suits your curriculum and your students. Use it to improve the reading climate in your school and the educational environment of the total school community. Most important, use it to foster the art of book reporting as an enjoyable educational experience for you and your students.

The author, a media specialist, would like to extend special thanks to the staff at Aurora Hills Middle School in Aurora, Colorado, especially to her media aide, to colleagues in the Aurora Public School District, and to educators in the greater Denver metropolitan area. A big thank-you goes to the students at Aurora Hills who have experienced and enjoyed the activities and made suggestions for modifying some of them.

Stamp of Approval

Students can commemorate their favorite book or author by making a "postage stamp." Have them draw a picture of one of the main characters from their favorite book on a sheet of paper. They can create a stamplike edge by punching out half circles around the paper's edges with a hole punch. Tell the students to write the title, author, and copyright date of the book on the stamp. Display the stamps in the classroom or media center. Students will see one another's stamps in the display and are sure to become interested in the books they have not read yet.

In addition, or for extra credit, ask students to draw or copy a picture of the author for another postage stamp. Have them write a letter to the postmaster general explaining why the author should be honored with a stamp.

A Report Card for Your Book

Congratulations! You have been chosen to grade the book you just read. Think carefully about your assignment. Judge the book fairly, and use this grading scale:

A = Excellent   **D** = Barely passing
B = Good   **F** = A flop!
C = So-so

Author's Name _____

Title of Book _____

Type of Book   ____ Nonfiction   ____ Fiction   ____ Biography

                ____ Science Fiction   ____ Fantasy   ____ Poetry

(Put a check in all the spaces above that apply to your book.)

Date of Report _____

Put a check mark beside everything that is true about your book.

____ Funny   ____ Sad

____ Interesting   ____ Boring

____ Captures the reader's attention   ____ Dull

____ Includes pictures   ____ No pictures

____ Suspenseful   ____ Predictable

____ Easy to read   ____ Difficult to read

____ Recommended   ____ Not recommended

I give this book a grade of _____.

Here are my reasons: _____

_____

_____

Student's Signature _____ **Date** _____

Good Plane Fun

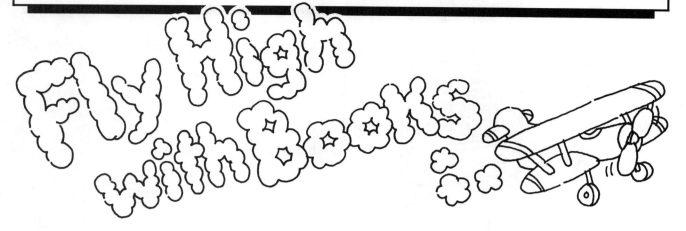

Instruct students to think about favorite books they have read recently. Have them fill in the lines below. If school policy allows and the weather is favorable, students may enjoy folding the paper into airplanes and flying them outside. Allow students to retrieve and read the "air mail" of another student.

....
Cut on dotted line

Name _____ Date _____

If I were flying to _____, I would

take the book _____

because _____

_____

_____

_____

_____

_____

_____

_____

_____

9

Get the Facts!

Materials: Lemon Juice
Toothpicks
Writing Paper

Make your students into book detectives with this "mysterious" activity. Have each select a favorite book and keep the choice a secret. Then tell them to write the author's name and a fact about the book in "invisible ink" (lemon juice, applied to the paper with toothpick "pens"). Let the paper dry for at least five minutes. Students can read the writing if they hold the paper up to a light source.

Have pairs exchange papers with each other. Each will read the other's message and track down the title of the book in the classroom collection or through the card catalog in the library/media center. If a student discovers a title, tell him or her to write the title on the original paper and return it to its owner.

If all students have been reading mystery books, or if you have read a mystery book orally to the class, you can vary this activity. Ask each student to write a question about the story in invisible ink, and then have students pair up to guess the answers to each other's questions.

Thumbs Up for Books

Have students trace one of their hands on a sheet of paper as shown in the illustration below. Instruct them to write the title across the back of their hand and the author's name on the wrist. Then have them write a positive comment about the book on the thumb and a fact about the book on each of the fingers. You may want to display the "hands" in the classroom or library/media center.

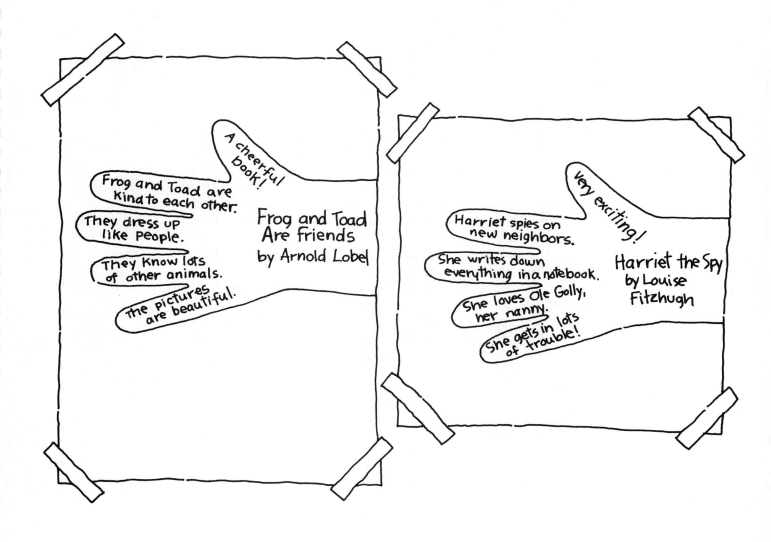

Readers' News

ANEWSworthy idea for combining interest in newspapers and books! Cut out the best-seller list and notices about book-related events from a local newspaper. They are usually found in the weekend/Sunday editions. Show these clippings to the class. Discuss them and post them on the wall. Some students may wish to bring in newspapers from home and share the book review section with their classmates. Other students may wish to write a letter to the editor, suggesting that the paper include a list of best-sellers in children's literature.

Small groups of students may create newspaper pages centering on books for kids. They can include book reviews and reports; library/media center happenings; a survey or list of kids' favorite books; articles about their favorite authors; and television programs, videos, or movies that were created from children's books. If a computer program is available for formatting a newspaper page, students may prefer to use it.

(Note: The activity sheet on page 13 has a book survey for kids to conduct. You may want to allow children to use the survey as part of this newspaper activity; the tallied results could make great "news"!)

Top Ten

Complete the following survey.

1. What is your favorite book? _____

2. Who is your favorite author? _____

3. How many books do you usually read in a month? _____

4. Do you prefer paperback or hardcover books? _____

5. Do you like fiction or nonfiction better? _____

6. Which of the following fiction subjects is your favorite?

   _____ **mystery**   _____ **adventure**

   _____ **science fiction**   _____ **romance**

   _____ **humor**   _____ **animals**

   _____ **family**   _____ **historical**

7. Do you usually carry a book with you wherever you go? _____

8. How often do you visit the school library/media center? _____

9. How often do you visit the public library? _____

10. How could you encourage your family and friends to read more?

    _____

    _____

    _____

    _____

You and your classmates may wish to compare your results. Or you may wish to survey other students and staff members, then tally the results.

Pretty as a Picture Postcard

This creative arts/language arts activity will reinforce practical writing skills. Make "postcards" for your students with white or light paper. If possible, make the cards with hard-stock paper so that students can put stamps on their cards and mail them. Instruct students to draw, color, or paint a scene from their book on one side of the postcard. Have them draw a vertical line down the middle of the other side. Help them address the postcard to a family member or friend. (Tell them the post office prefers that the name and address be printed in capital letters without punctuation.) Have them write a descriptive or creative comment about the book on the left side of the card.

James and the
Giant Peach
by Roald Dahl

James discovers a hole in the side of a peach and decides to climb in. He meets giant bugs inside the peach!

POST CARD

To: Mom + Dad
5 Main Street
Anytown, State
55505

Book Bingo

Students may create a Book Bingo game as a class, in small groups, or individually. Have students compile a list of 24 titles, 24 authors, or 24 characters, scenes, and events from the same book. Make up cards that match exactly the information on the lists. Shuffle the cards and play Book Bingo. Have the students mark an X on their square when that title, author, or character is called. The first student to get a row of X's diagonally, horizontally, or vertically is the winner. You may award the winner a bookmark, an extra visit to the library/media center, or a pencil.

You can copy the Book Bingo chart below.

		FREE		

Lights . . . Camera . . . . Action!

Cast the book for a movie using your favorite movie star.

1. Title _____

Author _____

2. I would choose _____.

for the leading role in my movie because

_____

_____

_____ .

3. The actual filming would take place in _____

because _____

_____ .

4. I would name the movie _____

_____ .

Student director's name _____

Date _____

Grandmother's Book Trunk

In the chart below, write a noun that begins with each letter. The nouns may be characters, events, scenes, or objects from a book your students have read. When you complete the list for yourself (do not distribute it to the class!), lead the class in the memory game Grandmother's Trunk. For example, you might say, "In my book, _____, there is an aardvark." The first student repeats "aardvark." You continue, "In my book, _____, there is a beach." The second student repeats "aardvark" and "beach." Continue. When a student misses a word or says the wrong word, he or she is out. Continue until the end of the alphabet or until all students are out.

A _____

B _____

C _____

D _____

E _____

F _____

G _____

H _____

I _____

J _____

K _____

L _____

M _____

N _____

O _____

P _____

Q _____

R _____

S _____

T _____

U or V _____

W _____

X, Y, or Z _____

It's in the Bag!

This activity motivates children to read books that are new to them and provides a review of familiar books.

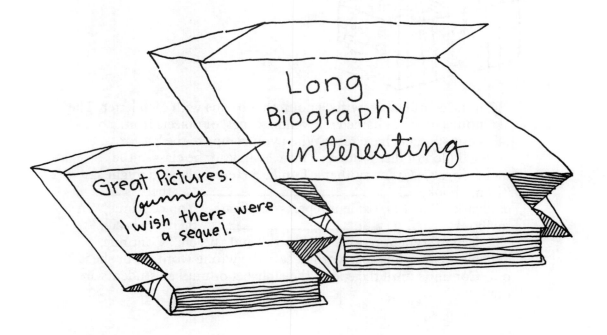

You will need:

Paper bags (lunch or grocery depending on size of books)

Magic marker, pen, or crayon for each student

This activity can be done as a class or with small groups. With the help of the reading teacher and/or the library/media specialist, select enough books for the whole class. Some titles may be familiar and popular, others new to students. Put each book in a bag and write the title on the bag. Arrange the students in a circle. Instruct them to take the book out of the bag and skim through it for a few minutes. Have each student write a short comment about the book on the bag, return the book to the bag, and pass it to the student to his or her right. Every book in its bag should be passed around the entire circle to allow each student to write a remark on the bag. At the end of a cycle, you may wish to have some students display the book to the class and read the comments aloud.

Book Stars

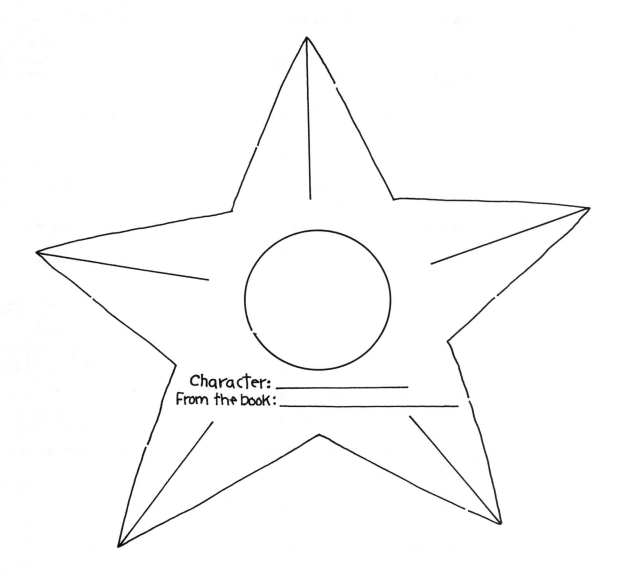

Character: _____
From the book: _____

Cut out the star above. Write the star character's name and book title on the lines of the star. Draw or trace a picture of the character in the circle. On each point of the star, write an adjective or a short phrase to describe him or her. Your teacher may post or hang the book stars in the classroom.

Name _____ Date _____

Title of Book _____

Simile and Metaphor

A simile is a comparison using *like* or *as.* Write five similes, each about a different character, scene, or event in a book that you have read.

1. _____

2. _____

3. _____

4. _____

5. _____

A metaphor is a comparison that doesn't use *like* or *as.* Write five metaphors, each about a different character, scene, or event.

1. _____

2. _____

3. _____

4. _____

5. _____

One-Minute Media Message

Instruct students to create an original message for a telephone answering machine, such as, "I can't come to the phone right now. I'm outside in a hammock reading *The Great Brain* by John D. Fitzgerald. It's a wonderful story about a boy genius. I'll call you back as soon as I finish the book."

If time and equipment allow, have students tape-record their messages and play the messages for the class. You may wish to invite another class to listen to the tape.

Author Time Line

Complete the time line with important events in your author's life. You may include publication dates of books that he or she wrote, the years spent in school, the date of the author's marriage, birth dates of his or her children, and important historical events that happened during the author's lifetime. Use biographical dictionaries, biographies, encyclopedias, almanacs, and the book itself to find "timely" information about the author.

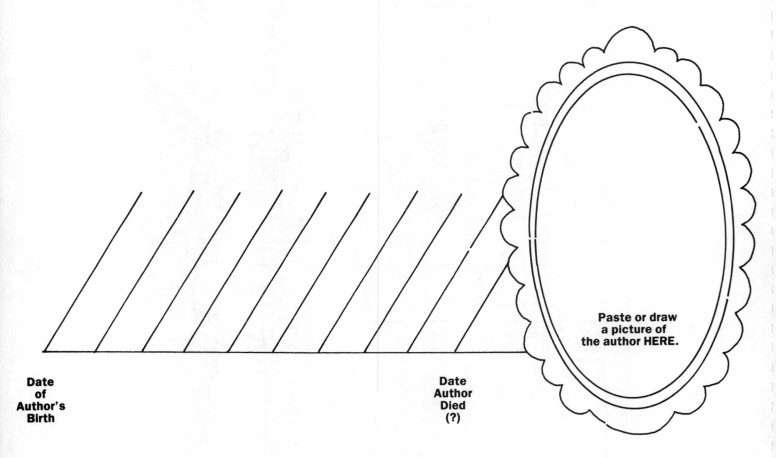

Date
of
Author's
Birth

Date
Author
Died
(?)

**Paste or draw
a picture of
the author HERE.**

TIME LINE:

THE LIFE OF _____

PSSST! Pupils Are Gossiping About Books!

Children will enjoy a new form of the game Gossip while they learn about books and improve their listening skills. Arrange students in a circle. Instruct them to announce the title of a book they have read. After a student tells the name of the book to the class, he or she whispers a fact about the book to the student on his or her left. This student repeats the fact to the next student. Continue around the circle until the "fact" is whispered to the originator. That student announces his or her original statement and the "new" one.

A Is for *Amazing Author . . . B* Is for *Best Book*

TITLE

_____ _____

_____ _____

_____ _____

_____ _____

_____ _____

_____ _____

_____ _____

AUTHOR'S LAST NAME

_____ _____

_____ _____

_____ _____

_____ _____

_____ _____

_____ _____

_____ _____

_____ _____

Spell out the letters of the title and author of a book you have read. Then write an adjective that begins with each letter. Use a dictionary, thesaurus, or the book itself to help you find words to describe the book and its author. Use the back of the sheet if you need more space.

TITLE

_____ _____

_____ _____

_____ _____

_____ _____

_____ _____

_____ _____

_____ _____

_____ _____

AUTHOR'S LAST NAME

_____ _____

_____ _____

_____ _____

_____ _____

_____ _____

_____ _____

_____ _____

_____ _____

Slide Show

Students can be coproducers of an instant audiovisual book show. Distribute two glass or plastic slides to each student. Instruct the students to write a book title in washable ink or magic marker on one slide. Have them draw a simple scene or character on the other slide. (Remind them to handle the slides carefully so that they do not smear the ink or drop slides on the floor.) Arrange the slides in a carousel with the title slide following each picture. Play some happy music. Enjoy the instant, student-produced slide show. You may wish to invite another class or parents to view the presentation.

Some students may wish to talk about their books when their slides are presented. Or a small group of students or an individual student may wish to draw several slides to describe a book. They may produce an audiotape of information or music to accompany their slide show.

Slides are available from camera stores for a nominal fee. They may be washed and reused. Ask for slides that have a 2 inches × 2 inches (5 cm x 5 cm) clear surface.

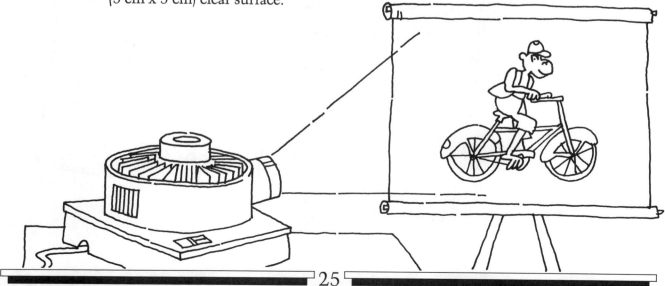

Book "Jigsaw" Puzzle

Students will enjoy making colorful jigsaw puzzles that illustrate their books. Have students reproduce the front covers of the books on hard-stock paper. Some students may wish to draw their own covers. Laminate the covers or attach clear contact paper to them. Cut them into puzzle shapes. Students may want to bring in shoe boxes or other empty boxes with lids to hold the shapes. The lids can also be decorated with the image of the book's cover.

Allow students to exchange puzzles; have them act as advisers if help is needed in putting the puzzles together. Some children may wish to take their puzzles home to share with family members.

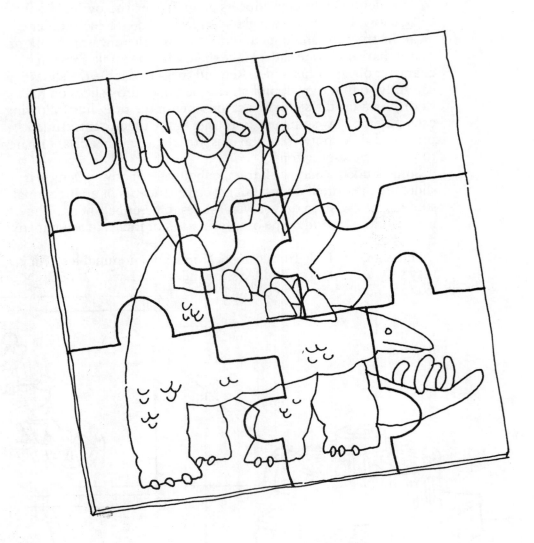

I-Openers . . .

I just read _____ by _____.

I really liked these characters: _____.

I would like to live in _____, where the story took place.

I would have changed the book title to _____.

I would have changed the opening line to _____.

I would have changed the ending to _____.

I would have added a chapter about _____.

I would recommend this book to _____.

I would write a sequel to the book in which the following happens: _____

_____.

I would name the sequel _____.

I liked this book (more/less) than the last book I read, which was titled

_____.

I have one more thing to say about this book: _____

_____

_____.

Book Quilt

For an eye-catching display, staple or tape butcher paper or a large sheet of paper on the wall. Cut paper or material into squares. Instruct students to draw or trace a simple scene from a book on each square. Have them print the title, author, and a creative description of the book. Glue, staple, or tape the completed squares onto the quilt. Change or add squares as students finish additional books.

The class may choose to create a theme quilt of classics, Caldecott or Newbery Medal winners, animal stories, or historical figures. Have students decorate the edge of the quilt with words or pictures to convey the theme.

HangBook

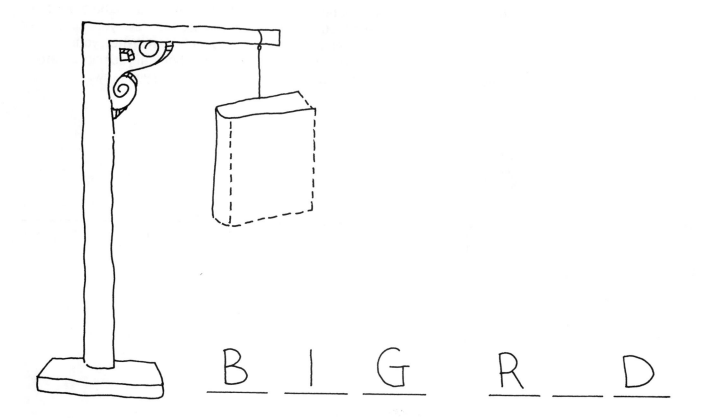

B I G _ _ R _ D

Children will enjoy this new version of an old favorite, Hangman. Ask the class to write the titles of several books that they have read recently. Collect the papers. Draw the "hanger" on the board or a transparency and play HangBook. Choose a book title and keep it a secret from your students. Next to the hanger, write a blank for each letter in the chosen title. Then proceed around the room, asking students to guess a letter that may be in the title. If the guess is correct, write the letter on the blank that you have drawn. If the letter is not in the title, draw a part of the book on the hanger. The game is over when a student guesses the title *or* when the drawing of the book is completed with incorrect guesses. Ask students not to participate in a game if the title is one they submitted.

Some students may wish to be the leader in the game; they may ask others to guess the titles they wrote down.

A Picture Is Worth a Thousand Words

Think of six things that happen in your book. Then draw the six scenes, in the order that they happen, in the rectangles below. Cut out and color the scenes. Give your six pieces to a classmate and see if he or she can put them in the correct order. When your classmate is finished, tell him or her the title and author of the book. If your classmate couldn't put the pictures in order, help out by explaining the scenes you drew.

Mark My Place!

This kids' keepsake is sure to generate interest in reading. Cut hard-stock paper into strips approximately 8 inches × 2 inches (20 cm × 5 cm) or ask printing shops to donate scraps. Instruct students to write the title, author, and a descriptive, positive comment about the book. Have them draw a scene from the book on the other side. Some students may wish to cut out a picture from an old magazine or catalog to illustrate the story. You may laminate the bookmarks if a laminator is available. As an alternative, cover the bookmarks with clear contact paper. Allow the students to exchange bookmarks to increase overall interest and excitement about reading.

Book Tree

Complete this tree to tell about the book you just read.

Write the author's name and the book title on the trunk. On each big branch, write the title or number of a chapter. If your book has no chapters, write a brief description of a scene. Write in chapters or scenes from left to right, in the order that they occur in the book.

Finally, on the smaller branches, write the different events that happened in each chapter or scene. Write them clockwise, in the order that they happened.

If this book tree is too small or doesn't have enough branches, draw your own on a larger sheet of paper. You may want to color your book tree and add background scenery that relates to the theme of your book.

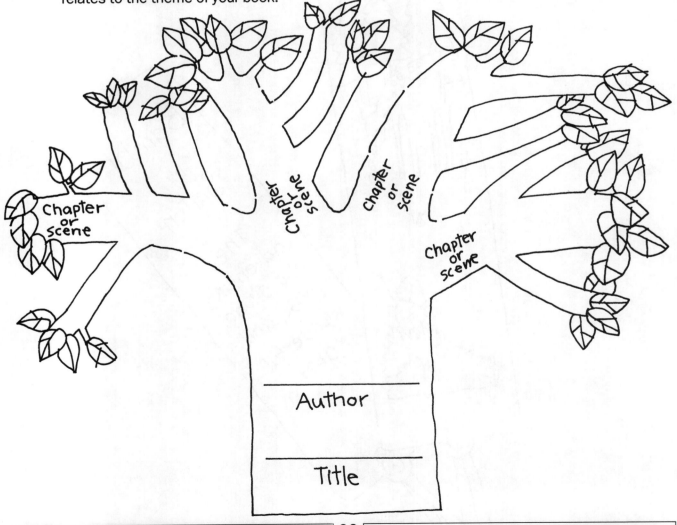

It's in the Cards

ere's a book version of the card game Concentration! Distribute two index cards to individual students. Ask them to think of a book they have read and write the title, the author, the names of characters, the chapter headings (if the book has chapters), descriptions of memorable scenes, and unusual vocabulary words on two cards. Have students shuffle the cards and spread them out facedown on the floor or a table. Students take turns picking up a card, looking at it, and trying to memorize its content and location. When a player picks up a card and knows where its match is, he or she can pick them both up. At the end of the game, the student with the most matched pairs of cards wins.

Advanced students may wish to create and play a more difficult version of the game. Tell them to write the title and author of a book on one card, and a description of the book on the matching card. Take a look at the cards before students play, to check the correctness of the matches. Two, three, or four students may play.

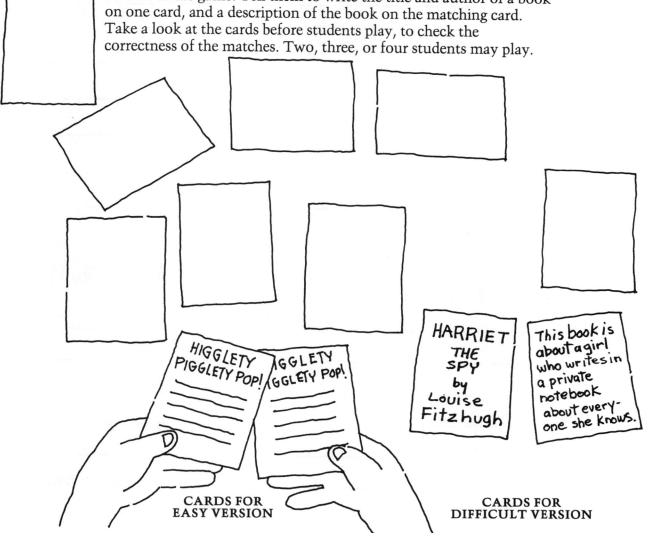

HIGGLETY PIGGLETY POP!

IGGLETY IGGLETY POP!

HARRIET THE SPY by Louise Fitzhugh

This book is about a girl who writes in a private notebook about everyone she knows.

CARDS FOR EASY VERSION

CARDS FOR DIFFICULT VERSION

The Six W's

Answer the six **W**'s about your book. The sixth **W** (**W**OW) is why you think the book is wonderful.

Title _____

Author _____

Who? _____

What? _____

Where? _____

When? _____

Why? _____

WOW! _____

Write a short book report using what you wrote in the blanks for all six **W**'s. Start and end with the word **W**OW!

WOW! _____

_____

_____

_____

_____

_____**WOW!**

Hats off to Books!

Discuss the expression "hats off" with your students. When people take their hats off to someone or something, it is a show of respect. Saying "Hats off to books!" is like saying "Hooray for books!" with a lot of respect thrown in. Distribute a sheet of paper to each child (use colorful paper if available). Have students fold the paper as shown below. You may wish to demonstrate the folding technique or allow partners to assist each other.

Instruct students to write the title and author of the book on the hatband. Have them cut out adjectives from old newspapers, catalogs, or magazines to describe their books, and paste them to the hat. Display the hats on or next to the books in the classroom or the media center with a banner that says, "Hats off to Books!"

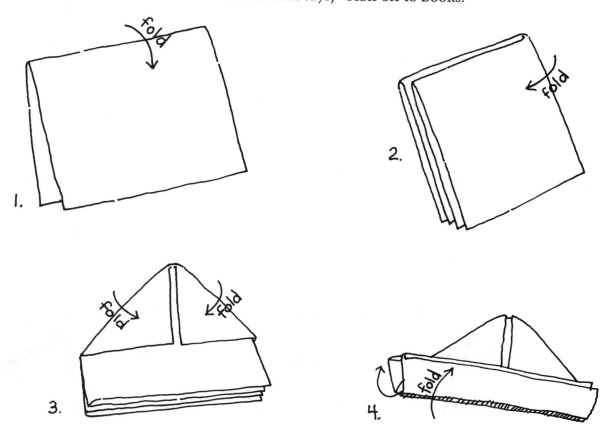

HOW TO FOLD THE PAPER HAT

It's All in a Name!

Discuss the titles of popular books with the class. Then divide the students into small groups. Instruct each group to choose a book that is familiar to all of the group members. Have them discuss the following:

1. why they think the author chose that particular title
2. the names of the characters
3. the titles of the chapters
4. other possible titles for the book and other names the group might choose for the characters
5. the titles of other books written by the same author

Have them research the meanings of names and places in the book, using reference tools in the library. Allow the students time to share their findings with the class.

F.B.I. Favorite Book Investigation

Your favorite book has been reported missing! Fill out the following report to help retrieve the book.

Title _____

Author _____

Publisher _____

Date of publication _____

Number of pages _____

Approximate size _____

Dewey decimal number (if known) _____

Distinguishing pictures or marks on cover _____

Condition of the book _____

Where and when the book was last seen _____

Persons who may know the possible whereabouts of the book

_____

_____

Any additional information that might be helpful to the F.B.I. (Favorite Book Investigators)

in locating your book

_____

_____

_____

_____

Name of student who filed the missing book report _____

_____

Date _____

Have a Ball with Your Book Reports!

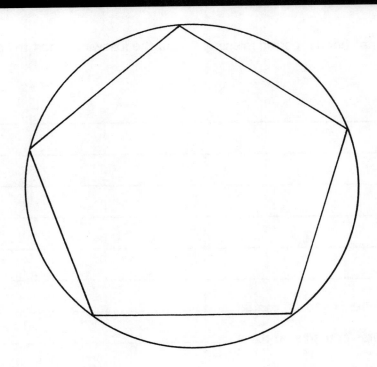

Y ou may wish to divide students into groups of twelve or
fewer for this activity. Reproduce twelve circles with
pentagons inside, as shown above, for each group. Instruct
students to think of a theme for their book ball, such as mystery,
science fiction, fantasy, and so on. Have them write a title, author,
and their reaction to the book on each pentagon. Tell them *not* to
write or draw outside of the pentagon. They may illustrate their
books if they like. Have them cut out each circle and fold on the
lines of the pentagon so that each fold faces up and the paper outside
the fold points toward the blank side. Staple or glue the pentagons
together, matching the tabs to make a ball. Hang the balls in the
classroom or media center.

You may wish to vary the activity by asking students to make an
entire ball about a single book. The ball could feature twelve
different scenes, or twelve different characters. Students can also
make a ball that features portraits of twelve different authors.

Flipped out over a Book!

Students will enjoy making a flip book to illustrate one of the scenes or characters in their book. For each flip book, they will need a notepad or several index cards. Tell them to choose a simple subject that moves, such as a person, an animal, or a boat. Draw the pictures in order; each picture should show a slight progression of movement (for example, a turn of the head, or a lifting of the left foot and then the right foot). If students use index cards, have them staple the pictures in order. As they flip through the notepad or the stapled cards, the subject will appear to move. Let them exchange flip books. The partner can try to guess who or what the subject is and which book is represented.

Recipe for Great Reading

Sheila Burnford's Recipe for Outdoor Adventure

INGREDIENTS:

2 dogs

1 cat

A dash of excitement

A stretch of Canadian wilderness

Add all the ingredients. Mix. Let simmer. Enjoy. Share with family or friends. Devour. Especially delicious on a rainy day. Animal lovers will find this recipe especially appealing.

Read this "recipe" to the class. Ask the students to guess the title of the book. (Answer: *The Incredible Journey)*

Distribute index cards to small groups of students. Instruct them to create a "recipe" for a favorite book they have read. At the top of the recipe, have them write "(Author)'s Recipe for (book's topic, or a positive expression about the book)." On the back of the recipe card, have them write the book's title. Store the cards in a recipe box and allow students to share their "food for thought" with the class.

Sheila Burnford's Recipe for Outdoor Adventure

INGREDIENTS:

2 dogs
1 cat
A dash of excitement
A stretch of Canadian wilderness

Add all the ingredients. Mix. Let simmer. Enjoy. Share with family or friends. Devour. Especially delicious on a rainy day. Animal lovers will find this recipe especially appealing.

Books Drive Me Wild!

Generate a discussion about license plates that authors or readers might own.

Talk about the license plates pictured above. Encourage students to think of additional license plates for authors or avid readers.

Then ask students to write their own license plates to show their enthusiasm for a book they have read or for an author whose work they enjoy reading. Ask them to limit the number of letters or numerals to ten.

Some students may wish to create a message to frame their license plate. Encourage them to use the colors of their state's or province's license plates.

Display the license plates and frames in the classroom or media center.

Sign of the Times

Book Title _____

Author _____

Consult the chart above, the astrology section of the newspaper, and books on astrology to complete the following sentences.

1. My zodiac sign is _____. I like books that are like me:

_____.

2. Although I don't know when my author was born, I think he/she is a

_____ because he/she _____
(zodiac sign)

_____.

3. The main character _____ in the book is probably a
(character's name)

_____ because he/she _____
(zodiac sign)

_____

_____.

Book-of-the-Month Club

This is an activity that you and your class can do once a month during the whole school year. Toward the end of each month, ask your students to write the title and author of a book that they read and loved that month. Have them also write (briefly) the reasons they think this book should be the "book of the month."

Have your students read their papers to the class one by one, or, if the class as a whole prefers, have them submit their papers to you so that you can read them all aloud without revealing the students' names. As the papers are read, students should keep their own running lists of the books they thought were the best choices for Book of the Month.

Finally, let students vote for the Book of the Month. Make a bulletin board that features the chosen book every month. If there is a tie, or if several books are very close in the running, you may want to feature them all as the Books of the Month. Your class may also wish to record all the Books of the Month for the whole school year on a special calendar.

A New Look for an Old Book

Round up or ask students to bring in some books that need a "new look," such as books with damaged or missing covers or classroom readers that have identical covers. Ask each student to browse through one of the books and create an original, interesting cover and a matching bookmark. Provide paper and tape for students. You may give instructions for folding paper into bookcovers or give assistance to students who need help. Ask students to write the title and author's name and draw a picture on the front cover. Then have them repeat the title and author's name on the spine, and write a short synopsis on the back cover. Display the "new" books in the classroom.

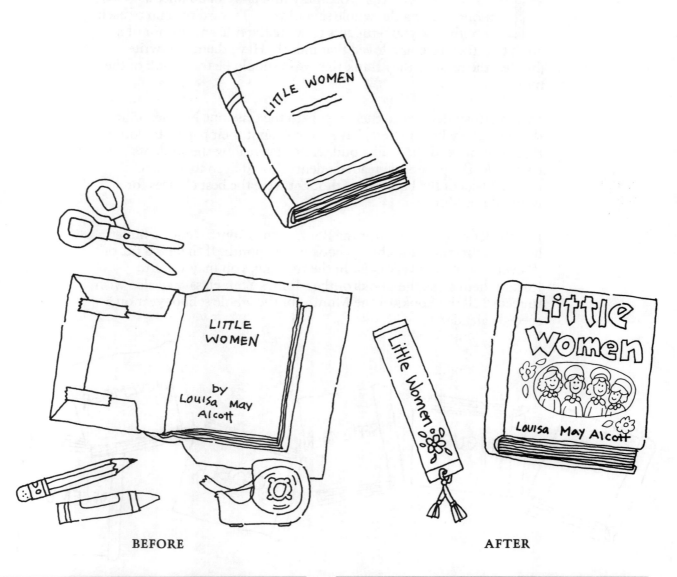

BEFORE   AFTER

Books Will Take You Everywhere!

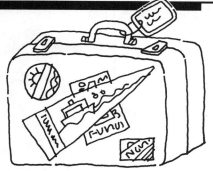

Post a world map in the classroom. Ask students to create a luggage tag for a book they have read. Tell them to write the title and author's name and any geographical areas that are mentioned in their book. If no locations are mentioned, suggest that they guess where the story took place by thinking about how the characters live, talk, and dress.

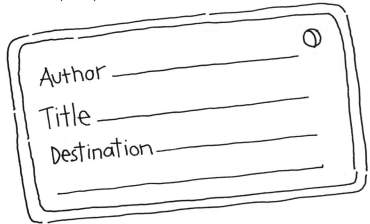

Distribute to each student an index card in which a hole has been punched. Have students string a piece of string or yarn through the hole and attach the string to a push pin that they place near the geographical area on the world map. Several strings can be attached to the same push pin.

Books Alive!

Pretend that you are a "live" book. Finish the thoughts of a book that you just read.

I am _____.
(title)

I was created by _____.
(name of author)

I have pictures drawn by _____.
(name of illustrator)

I was published by _____.
(publisher)

I came to life in _____ in _____.
(city, state, country)   (year)

I want to live in _____.
(name of library, house, or room)

I wish my cover were made of _____ and decorated with

_____.

I want to be a friend of _____.
(main character)

I would like to share a shelf with _____.
(name of another book)

by _____.
(author)

I would like to share my story with _____.
(name of a person)

If a movie director wanted to make a movie out of me, I would call the movie

_____.

If I had only one wish, it would be _____.

_____.

Place That Face

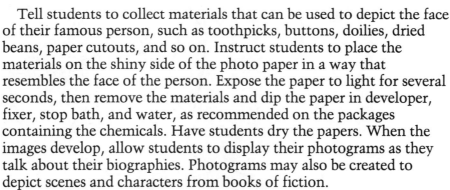

George Washington

Introduce students to creating photograms to illustrate their book reports on famous people. A photogram is a picture created without using a camera. You will need a darkroom and the following materials:

photographic paper, 4 inches × 5 inches
   (10 cm × 13 cm)
miscellaneous items for collage
light or lamp
developer
fixer
stop bath

Tell students to collect materials that can be used to depict the face of their famous person, such as toothpicks, buttons, doilies, dried beans, paper cutouts, and so on. Instruct students to place the materials on the shiny side of the photo paper in a way that resembles the face of the person. Expose the paper to light for several seconds, then remove the materials and dip the paper in developer, fixer, stop bath, and water, as recommended on the packages containing the chemicals. Have students dry the papers. When the images develop, allow students to display their photograms as they talk about their biographies. Photograms may also be created to depict scenes and characters from books of fiction.

If a darkroom is not available, students can create a silhouette of a famous person. Have them trace or draw his or her profile. Use the overhead projector to enlarge each one for the whole class to see, or post them in the classroom or library/media center.

Wrap It Up!

Distribute a sheet of butcher paper or newsprint to each student. Ask students to design wrapping paper for a book they have read. Have them create designs or scenes on the paper that would let others guess the title of the book. Instruct them to draw characters, scenes, or familiar items from their book. They can make patterns with characters or objects. Some may wish to depict several scenes in sequence.

Have students wrap the book using the decorated paper. Ask them to make a gift tag on which they have written a slogan, comment, or short summary of the book, but be sure to tell them not to include the title or author!

Ask each student to show the wrapped book to the class. Let the class guess the title and author of the wrapped book before it is unwrapped by the designer.

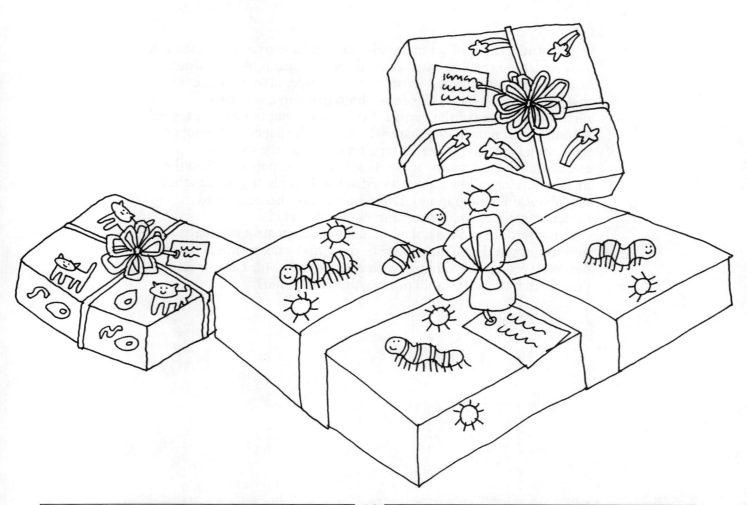

Group Book Reports

To whet your students' interest in reading something new, ask the librarian or media specialist at your school to give a book talk about recent titles. Then divide the class into small groups, and for each group select a book that all the members can read at the same time. Be sure that the book is new to everyone in the group, and keep in mind that each member of the group will be reporting on one section of the book.

When all members of a group have read and discussed their book, have them divide the book into sections and choose a section on which they would like to give a report. You may have all students in a group follow the same report format, or let the group plan a "cabaret" of different types of reports. Allow each group to report their book in its entirety to the class.

Fishing for Catchy Words

Ask students to make a list of at least ten unusual or intriguing words as they read their books. Tell them to print the words on fish cutouts. If the word is short, have students cut out a small paper fish; if the word is long, have them cut out a larger fish. Some students may wish to create a face on their fish that says something about the word: a happy face for *euphoric,* a sad face for *morose,* and so on.

You may select a group of students to cover a wall or bulletin board with blue or green paper. Have them attach a light tree limb or something else that resembles a fishing pole. Tie string or twine to the end of the fishing pole. Let students glue or staple their fish with "catchy words" to the paper.

Students may wish to consult a dictionary for exact meanings of their ten words displayed on the bulletin board.

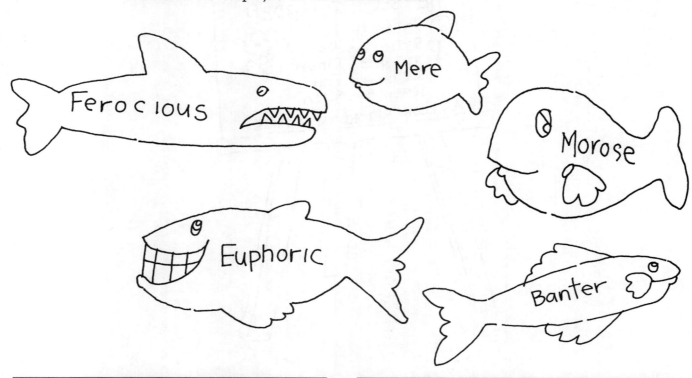

Wheel of Fiction

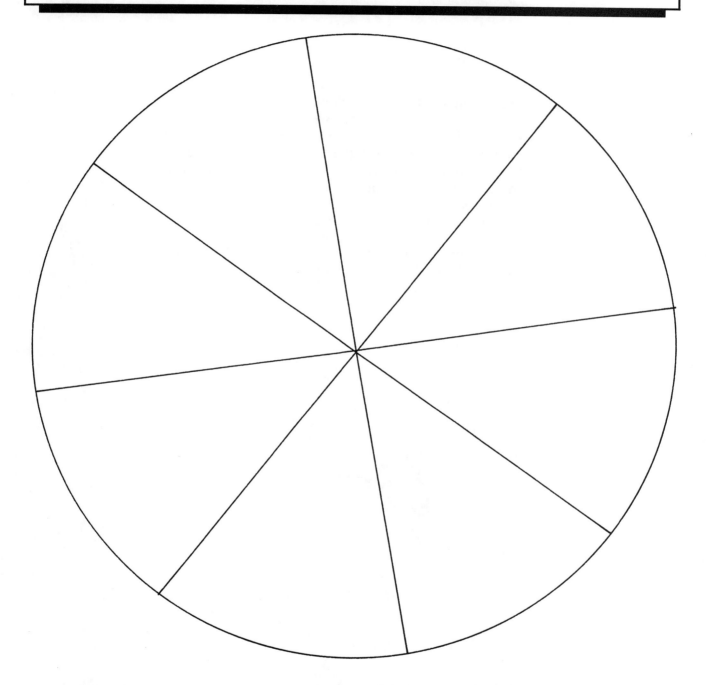

Think about the action and adventure in a fiction book you have read. In eight consecutive sentences, summarize the plot of the story, using as many action verbs as you can. Write each sentence on a different spoke of the wheel.

Creative Comics

Ask each student to bring in old newspapers from home. Have students read the comic sections, then ask each student to select a favorite comic strip. Instruct the student to mask out the words in the dialogue balloons with white labels or paper. Tell them to think about a book they have read and write captions in the balloons that would relate to their book. The comic-strip characters may describe a scene in the book, comment or critique the book, or poke fun at a character in the book. Have students glue the "new" comic strip onto sturdy paper. Above the comic strip, students should write a comic-strip title that includes the book title, such as "Dave and Sue Rap about *Soup*." You may wish to post the creative comics in the classroom for everyone to share.

My Mini-autobiography

Complete the sentences on the squares on both sides of the paper. Start with square 1 (include name), turning the paper as you finish the sentences. Fold the paper on the lines so that square 1 is on the top, followed by consecutive squares. When folded, staple the left side of the mini-autobiography. Cut off the top fold to make separate pages.

5. I have ———— brother(s) and
(number)
———— sister(s). Their names are
(number)

4. I have ———— pet(s) named
(number)

8. A famous person I admire most is

————————————————————

————————————————————

1. The title of my autobiography is

————————————————————

————————————————————

53

My Mini-autobiography

Your teacher may wish to read the autobiographies to your class (omitting your name) and allow your classmates to guess who the author is. After all the autobiographies are read, they could be stapled or sewn together for a collective class autobiography.

3. My favorite school subject is _____

6. My favorite sport/activity is _____

2. I was born in _____ (city/state)

in _____ (year).

7. In the future I would like to be a(an)

_____.

Sounds Good to Me!

Before students begin reading their next book, instruct them to "listen" to the story. Tell them to keep a list of words and phrases that appeal to sense of hearing, such as the rustling of leaves, the ringing of a telephone, a knock on a door, a baby's cry, the barking of a dog, and so on. If tape recorders are available, allow students to record as many actual sounds as possible. Some students may wish to re-create the sounds. Other students may wish to read aloud the "sound" expressions they see in the book. Have the class guess the names of the books that contain the sounds. If appropriate to your students' level, you may wish to discuss onomatopoeia with them.

All Bottled Up

Ask each student to bring in a small plastic bottle with a wide opening. Instruct each student to write a short, enthusiastic note by or about a character in their book. Students can work with partners to write interesting, creative messages. Tell students to roll or fold the note carefully and insert it in the bottle. Cap or cover the tops of the bottles and have students exchange them with partners. Have students repeat the procedure until they all have had a chance to read five or six messages. Encourage students to share their reactions to the messages.

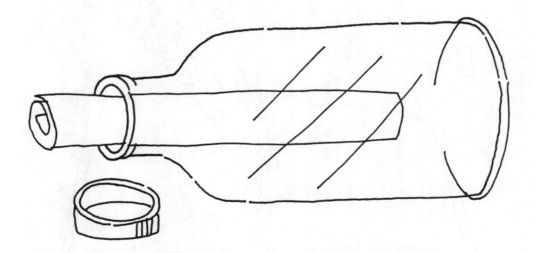

My Reading Calendar

Illustrate the top of the calendar by drawing or cutting out pictures that relate to your book. Fill in the dates of the current month on the individual squares. Each day, write the amount of pages you read and the time you spent reading the book. You may wish to mark the dates when you are 1/4, 1/2, and 3/4 of the way through the book.

SUN	MON	TUE	WED	THU	FRI	SAT

Pockets of Poetry

With the help of the reading teacher and the librarian/media specialist, introduce students to a variety of poetry books. You may read some of the poems to the class, or ask for a volunteer to read.

After students complete a book of poetry, give them a book pocket and book card from the library/media center. If cards and pockets are not available through media services, they may be constructed from hard-stock paper and lined paper.

Instruct students to decorate the book pockets with a scene from one of the poems in the book. Have them write the author and title of the book on the top of the card and a short comment about the book on the first couple of lines. Have them sign their names after their comments. Post the envelopes on the board or put them in an accessible place. As other students read the same book, have them add their own comments and signatures to the card. Add additional blank cards to the pocket as needed.

Want Ads for Readers

Wanted A reader who likes dog stories. Flexible hours. Start anytime. Satisfaction guaranteed. Call the public library for further details.

Available for Lending *The Velveteen Rabbit* by Margery Williams

Highly recommended for young children. In excellent condition, even though it's been read over and over.

Lost Answers to the name of Lassie. Last seen wearing a white and brown jacket. Over 50 years old.

Create similar classified ads for books you have read.

Wanted: _____

_____

_____

Available for Lending: _____

_____

_____

Lost: _____

_____

_____

If you like, you can create even more ads.
Continue on the back of this sheet.

A People's Party for Books!

Have students write a letter to their parents, guardians, grandparents, teachers, and neighbors inviting them to a book party before or after school. Ask the adults to think about their favorite childhood books. You may wish to provide simple refreshments; the children might enjoy naming the foods after popular titles, for example, Peter Rabbit's Carrots, The Great Brain's Brownies, Charlie's Chocolates, and so on.

At the party, ask the adult guests to write the names of their favorite childhood authors on name tags and wear them as they circulate. Encourage children to ask questions about the authors and their books. Ask the guests to volunteer information about their favorite books to the children.

After the party, have the children write thank-you notes to the people who attended the book party. You may also wish to follow up the party with a class discussion about children's literature that was popular a generation (or more) ago.

Realia Reports

Ask students to collect common, simple objects and materials. Provide a box in the classroom where they can deposit miscellaneous items such as combs, toothpicks, pennies, paper clips, keys, paper fasteners, string, play money, candy wrappers.

Instruct the students to write creative comments about their books with some of the items. Have them glue or tape the materials on hard-stock paper. You may wish to display the realia reports in the classroom.

Show them some examples, such as:

I' so excited about the book I just read.

I really did read the best book! You would have to the whole library to find a better

The suspenseful plot will you along until you are dying to know the ending!

The to understanding this book is . . .

Rebus Riddles

Below is an example of a **rebus** about Nate and his enormous egg. A rebus is a sentence made of words, letters, and pictures. When you read a rebus aloud, it sounds like it's *all* words!

Create your own rebus riddle about a book you have read. Show your paper to your teacher and then exchange papers with a partner.

QUESTION   🧙 📕 S about N8 and a GR8 🐔 BAWK! BAWK! N her 🕸 ?

ANSWER   The N or 🐭 ⬭ by ◖ ER 🍞 WORTH!

(The solution to this rebus is upside down at the bottom of the page.)

Use this space for *your* rebus riddle:

Question: Which book is about Nate and a great hen in her nest?
Answer: The Enormous Egg by Oliver Butterworth!

Mystery Boxes

Individual students or small groups may wish to report on a book in the mystery genre by creating a mystery box. Students may use shoe boxes, hat boxes, grocery boxes or lunch boxes; boxes with hinged lids are especially effective for a presentation. Have them cover and decorate the outsides of their boxes with "strange" pictures or words from their book. Instruct them to make or collect clues that relate to their mystery book. They may wrap the clues in paper before placing them in the box.

Display the mystery boxes in the room for a few days, to give students a chance to examine the clues in each box and think about what each "mystery book" might be. Then designate a day for students to stand up one by one (or group by group) and ask the class, "Has anyone guessed what *this* mystery book is?" Either someone will guess correctly, or the creator of the box will have to reveal the title and author of the mystery book. Then a discussion of each clue in the box can follow, to whet the class's interest in the book's content.

Name _____ **Date** _____

Title of Book _____

Make a Face Book Report

Finish the following statements about your book. Be creative. Make up a face and an adjective for the last sentence.

I felt sad  when this happened in the book: _____
_____
_____.

I liked  the character _____ because
_____
_____.

I was happy  when _____
_____.

The story puzzled me when _____
_____
_____.

When I finished the book, I felt  and  and  !

_____   _____

Endangered Books!

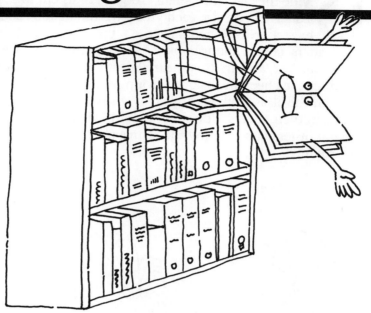

HELP! Don't let a book become endangered or extinct. Write a letter to the author or the publisher of one of your favorite books. Explain why this book should always be kept in print and why kids of all ages should have access to this book in stores, homes, schools, and public libraries everywhere.

Dear _____,

_____

_____

_____

_____

_____

Sincerely,

_____ Date _____

Three Cheers for Books!

Divide the class into small groups. Ask them to select a group leader. Encourage each group to think about books they have all read. Then have them brainstorm and create cheerleaders' cheers about books. Ask them to make up a cheer for a title, an author, and an illustrator. Allow each group leader to introduce the cheer and ask the group participants to perform the cheer for the class. Some groups may wish to include simple physical actions in their cheers. You may wish to videotape the cheers and/or invite another class to enjoy the "three cheers for books" performance.

Books with Weather Themes

Have your students brainstorm a short list of different kinds of weather. Divide your students into as many groups as there are types of weather on your list, and do the following:

- Have each student in a particular group read a book about the weather condition that their group is assigned. Some students can be assigned nonfiction and some can read fiction.

- Have each group research their weather condition, using encyclopedias or other reference tools.

- Finally, have each group give a report. First have the group report their collective research findings about the weather condition. Next have each student in the group give a brief review of the book he or she read.

Encourage students to embellish their presentation with "scenery" (snowflakes hanging from the ceiling, an electric fan blowing to represent strong wind), "costumes" (such as gear for foul, warm, or cold weather), and "sound effects" (recordings or vocal imitations of thunder or howling wind). Students can also sing songs or recite poems about the weather condition they are reporting on, to "warm up" their audience for their presentation!

Book-o-Mime

Assign or select small groups of students to read and report on a book the whole class has read. Tell each group that they are going to write a book-o-mime—a pantomime in which the basic plot of their book (or of a chapter from their book) will be acted out. All the members of the group are responsible for writing and editing the script. For each group, choose a director. Tell the director that his or her role is to give oral directions to the players as they rehearse the pantomime. The other group members will be the actors. The actors may each be given separate direction, or may all be directed to perform the same movements at once. Allow each group to perform for the class. The other class members can try to guess which book the book-o-mime portrays.

Action Map

Think about the scenes, the character(s), and the events in the book you just read. Decide on at least ten scenes where action took place, and in what sequence. Make a map of the "itinerary" of one or more of the characters through the book—that is, follow them on your map from place to place according to what they do in the story. If you "trace" the path of more than one character, use a different color for each character's trail. Draw the map neatly and clearly, using arrows as necessary to show direction and sequence. You may wish to exchange papers with a classmate to see if he or she can follow the action and decide from which book the map was drawn.

Telebook

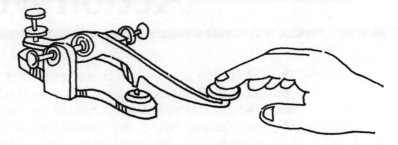

Discuss the history and current status of telegrams with the class. Some students may wish to research telegrams in the library/media center; others may wish to find out the current cost of sending a telegram. Have all students compose a telegram about a book they have read. Encourage them to be concise.

To: Yule Likett

From: Fonda Books

Just finished the most exciting book. STOP. Title is *Hatchet*. STOP. Author is Paulsen. STOP. Exciting story about survival. STOP. Find it at your school library. STOP.

Assign each student the name of another student who will receive his or her telegram. You may wish to collect the telegrams and assign a student messenger to deliver the telegrams. Students may wish to share the telegrams they receive with the class.

A Writer's Ideas

Think about the book you just read. Think about how the author may have gotten his or her ideas for the story. The author may have based his or her story on a famous folk tale, on a personal experience, or on a historic period or event. Write the title of the book and the author's first and last name in the circle. On each line coming from the circle, write about one of the different subjects or situations the author may have had in mind when writing his or her book. You may want to read about your author in a reference book; it may tell you something about where the author's ideas came from.

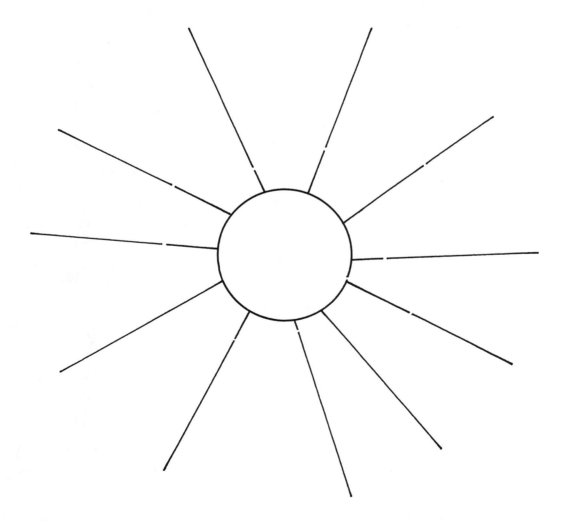

Sneak Preview

This activity is an exercise in both retrieving fiction books from the library and reporting on them. Tell students to find a book in the fiction section of the library written by an author whose last name begins with the same letter as their own last name. Arrange them alphabetically in a circle by last names. Tell them they have 5 to 10 minutes to sneak a peek at their book and 1 minute to "sell" the book to the class. Have them warm up by announcing the author, title, and at least one positive, creative sentence about the book. If a video camera is available, you may wish to tape and replay the sneak-preview session.

Around the World with Reading

Author _____

Title of Book _____

Price of Book _____ (Round price to the nearest dollar.)

   If no price appears on the book, compare it with a similar book and use that as the price. Use the currency of the country and an up-to-date encyclopedia, this year's almanac, or the daily newspaper to complete the following sentences. Calculate the price based on the price in the United States. Exclude international costs, shipping, and so on.

Japanese children would pay _____.

This book would cost _____ in England.

The price of the book in Germany would be _____.

A store in France would charge _____.

Australians would pay _____.

A storekeeper in Spain would charge you _____.

If I bought the book in _____ I would pay _____.
                        (select a country)

Complete the following sentence.

The book would be a great value anywhere in the world because

_____

_____

_____

True or False?

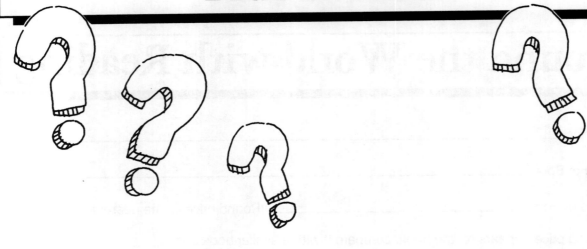

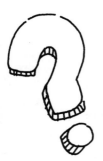

Arrange the students in small groups by similar book interests. Instruct them to select a book they have all read. Have them think of true and false statements about the book as they browse through it together. Encourage all team members to participate. The team "secretary" lists the true and false statements on a piece of paper. Allow each team to present its statements to the class. The team reporter reads aloud each statement; the class votes on the truth or falsity of the statement by a show of hands. The team gets a point if it fools the majority of the class. Record the team results on the board.

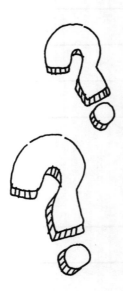

Sold on Subjects

Student book recommendations are sure to help other students in book selections. Instruct students to use large index cards for these mini–book reports. Have them use a format similar to that below.

Subject of Book _____
(capital letters)

Author _____

Title of Book _____

Character(s) _____

Setting _____

Description (1–2 sentences)

_____

_____

Why This Book Is Recommended

_____

_____

_____

_____

File the cards alphabetically by subject in a classroom box that is readily available to every student. If a computer is available, students may wish to make a classroom database.

Mystery Report

Ask each child to write a mystery report poem, beginning with a couplet such as:

There once was a mystery, which I read
With the covers pulled over my head.

If possible, dim the lights in the classroom (or shut them off). You may ask children to close their eyes. Student reporters attach their mystery reports to black paper. They read their reports by flashlight. Encourage students to use appropriate sound and visual effects to accompany their reports. At the conclusion of the mystery report, discuss with the class the popularity of mystery and ghost stories. Some students may then wish to tell their favorite mystery or ghost stories to the class.

Book Flowers

This activity makes it fun for students to report their progress as they read. Have each student cut a big circle from construction paper and write his or her name in the center. This will be the middle of individual book flowers. Each time a student reads a book, he or she will write the title and author on a petal and attach it to the circle. You can create a bulletin board of flowers for your classroom, or post the flowers in the library/media center.

Alternatively, have groups of students create book flowers. Assign each group a topic for reading, and have each student find a book on that topic. Each student should contribute a petal with a title and the name of the author to the construction-paper circle. In the middle of the circle, write the topic.

**INDIVIDUAL'S
BOOK FLOWER**

**GROUP'S
BOOK FLOWER**

No, None, Nobody, Nothing

Put a check by all of the true statements about your book.

_____ There are no illustrations.

_____ There is no index.

_____ There is no table of contents.

_____ There are no animals in the story.

_____ Nobody would want to read this book more than once.

_____ The book contains no biographical information about the author.

_____ There is no glossary.

_____ There is no other book as good as this one.

_____ There is no way anyone could read this book in a week.

Write five more "no's" about your book.

_____

_____

_____

_____

_____

Oscar Awards for Books!

You've heard of the Oscars. They're special awards for the best movies. Now you can create Oscar awards for your favorite books, authors, illustrators, characters, settings, and story plots!

First, complete your ballot and cut it out:

Name _____ Date _____

NOMINEES FOR

Best Book: (Title) _____ (Author) _____

(Illustrator) _____

Best Author Ever: _____

Best Illustrator Ever: _____

Best Character: (Name) _____

in (Book Title) _____

Best Setting: _____

in (Book Title) _____

Best Plot: (Tell What Happens) _____

_____

in (Book Title) _____

Now hold your own awards ceremony for books! You and your classmates can tally everyone's votes in each category. There are six categories, so you will be giving six Oscars. If you have a classmate whom you think is a good speaker, suggest that he or she be the master of ceremonies (the one who announces the Oscar winners to the class)!

Author for a Day!

Complete the following sentences as if you were the author of a book you read.

I am _____.

I was born on _____ at _____.
                  (date)   (place)

I wrote the book called _____.

My favorite character is _____.

My favorite line in the book is _____.

My favorite scene in the book is _____.

My favorite author is _____.

My favorite book is _____.

I wrote the book because _____.

I think my book will be read and enjoyed for a long time because _____

_____

_____.

You may wish to read your statement—or an even longer one—to the class. Allow classmates to question you about your life as a famous author!

Note to Teacher: If video equipment is available, you may tape the student presenting his or her "author autobiography." If school policy allows, let the student(s) take the videotape home to show to family members.

A Thinking Cap

Bring in a hat from home. It can be any kind of hat that you believe will help you to think about books!
Fill in the sign below, cut it out, and attach it to the front of your hat. Wear the hat to class on the day your teacher asks you to, and let your classmates read it.

I'm thinking of a book I just read.

The book's title is _____.

I think I'd like to read another book by the same author.

The author's name is _____.

I think I would recommend this book to _____

_____.

I think this book has a _____ending.

If I could, I would change this about the book: _____

_____.

I have one more important thought about this book: _____

_____.

Suits Me to a T!

Here's a hands-on activity to promote favorite books or book characters. Instruct the students to write the title of a favorite book or the name of a favorite character on a sheet of construction paper. You may wish to have students tape or pin the "promo papers" on their clothing. Allow them to circulate around the classroom, answering questions and relating information about their favorite "finds."

Some students may wish to bring in a blank T-shirt from home. Allow them to paint their shirts with fabric colors or indelible markers. They may wish to decorate the back or the sleeves of the shirt with scenes from their books. You may hang the T-shirts on a clothesline in the classroom, or encourage students to wear their shirts to school on a specially designated Friday.

Fan of Fiction

Write "fan"-tastic facts about a favorite fiction book on each of the lines below, in between the lines for Title and Author. You may decorate the edges. Fold into a fan and staple the bottom. Your teacher may wish you to exchange fans with other students or hang them in the classroom or media center.

. . . . .cut along this line . . . .

Title: _____

_____

_____

_____

_____

Author: _____

A Perfect Book Report Form

What kind of book report do you like best?

You have a perfect opportunity to design a perfect book report form. Think about what should be included in a book report. What's most important about a book? What's the best way to describe a good book to someone else? Ask your friends, teachers, and family members for their ideas about book reports.

Use the space below to design the perfect book report form. Then make your final draft on a separate piece of paper. Remember to include room for the title, author, and the student's name. You may wish to draw pictures or decorate the edges with illustrations.

Your teachers and classmates may vote on the best form, which may then be duplicated and used for actual book reports.

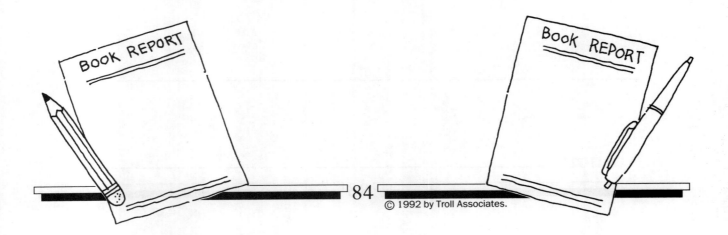

A Classic

Discuss the meaning of classic books with the class. Tell them that classic books have a universal theme, are often highly thought of and excellently written, appeal to many people, and have a permanent place in the world of literature.

Arrange the students in a circle. Distribute a different classic novel or fairy tale to each child. You may wish to insert a bookmark or a slip of paper between pages that are especially interesting and exciting. Play zesty classical music as students browse through the books and make notes on the slips of paper. Have each look at his or her book for a few minutes before passing it to the person next to him or her. After each student has seen about ten books, encourage students to briefly discuss any of the books that appeal to them. You might ask them to complete the sentence orally or on paper, "I think this classic book will be around a long time because . . ."

Encourage students to keep the classics alive by instructing them to design a new cover for a classic—a cover that will appeal to readers in the twenty-first century. You may wish to display the covers in the classroom or in the library/media center.

A Jewel of a Book

Trace the jeweled crown below onto two sheets of paper. Cut out both tracings and tape the pieces together. Write the author and title and comments about the book on the crown. Decorate with cutouts of jewels from construction paper or from magazine pictures. If poster board is available, use it for a sturdier crown. Be prepared to answer questions about your valuable, treasured book.

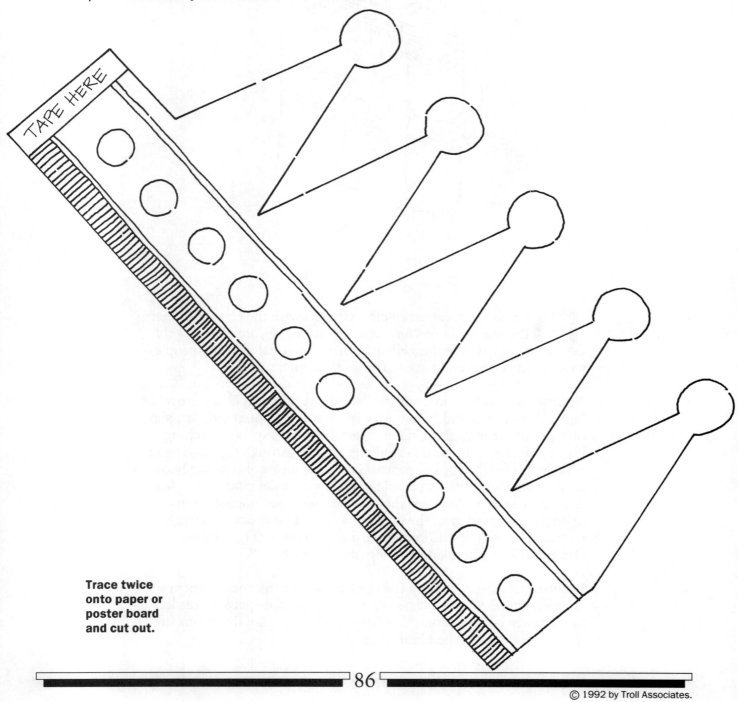

TAPE HERE

Trace twice onto paper or poster board and cut out.

Ghost Chapter

Think about a book with chapters that you read recently. How did you like the story? Did you wish that *more* had happened? Here's your chance to write a ''ghost chapter''—a chapter that might have appeared in a book but didn't! You may write it for the beginning, somewhere within the book, or the end of the story. If you choose to include it at the end, you may wish to create a never-ending book, that is, an incomplete story that leaves the reader wondering.

Author _____

Title of book _____

Position of ghost chapter in the book _____

_____

Summary of ghost chapter

_____

_____

_____

_____

_____

_____

_____

Puppets on the Go!

Show students how to create a movable puppet suspended by two hands. Have them draw people or animal puppets on poster board. They may need assistance in cutting them out and attaching a small poster-board tube to the top of each puppet. Instruct them to tie a loop of string through the tube; have them attach string to the head of the puppet. Tape the other end of the string to a pencil to allow the puppet to move. Students hold a puppet up by the two strings and move it as desired. The puppets can bring life to a book report or puppet play as they run, walk, or jump.

Younger students may wish to create puppets out of paper lunch bags. Have them draw heads or faces on the top half of the bags, insert their hands, and move them to make the puppets come to life.

Some students may wish to sew or glue materials on old socks, gloves, or mittens to represent the characters in a favorite book.

Other students may wish to cut out strips of paper, draw a simple face in the center, tape them around a finger, and bring life to these characters by moving their fingers.

What's My Line?

Stimulate interest in biographies by letting students participate in a guessing game that's similar to the old "What's My Line?" television game show! This is a game that can be played with one "mystery guest" at a time, over many class days. Pick a volunteer to be the first mystery guest. Have him or her choose and learn all about a famous person whom the whole class has studied, or whom you can be fairly sure all your students have heard something about. Tell the student not to tell anyone which famous person he or she has chosen (except *you*—you will probably want to be sure the famous person can be guessed by the class). The student should make up a list of ten hints about the identity of the person.

Begin Round One of the game by having the student pretend to be the famous person he or she chose. The student should begin by reading five of the hints. Then give the class a chance to guess. If no one guesses correctly, have the mystery guest read his or her other five hints one by one. The first student to guess the guest's identity gets to be the next mystery guest.

Famous children's book authors can also be the subject of this game. Students can make the guessing tricky by saying something like "I wrote a book about a brave lad and his dog," instead of revealing any of the author's book titles in the hints.

A Book on Trial

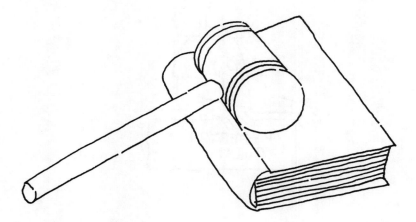

In this "courtroom" in which a book is tried, students voice their opinions about a book and listen to the opinions of other students.

Allow the class to elect a prosecuting attorney and a defense attorney; encourage the students to choose good speakers. The class may also vote on which book will be tried; it should be a book that has been read by all or most of the students. Allow small groups of students to decide what charges should be filed against the book, its characters, or its author. Help them decide what consequences may result if a book is found "guilty" of the charges.

Some students may wish to research court proceedings so that the trial is held in a realistic manner. If the parent of a student is in the legal profession, you may wish to invite him or her to assist in the proceedings.

Various students will serve as the judge, jury, witnesses, and author. Summonses may be written to the media specialist, teacher, or reading specialist requesting his or her appearance as special witnesses to the book's "character."

Encourage students to think through the charges thoughtfully and deliberately. Set a time limit for attorneys to make their cases, and for the jury to reach a verdict.

You're on the Right Track!

Students will stay on the right track as they add ties to the "Reading Railroad." To make the railroad tracks, you may staple or tape parallel strips of crêpe paper or adding-machine paper around the room. As students finish a book, have them write the author, title, a sentence that describes the book, and their name on a paper railroad tie. Tell them to attach the tie to the track. Students will enjoy watching the track grow.

Students may wish to create a "Ticket to Adventure." You may post these around or near the Reading Railroad.

Ticket to Adventure

Want plenty of action-filled adventure?

Travel with _____ in
            (character)

_____ !
           (title)

This journey takes _____ _____ .
           (number)   (days/weeks/months)

I ought to know—I read the book!

Ticket issued by _____

Date _____

Rhyme Time!

Create a limerick about your book or one of the characters in it.

_____

_____

_____

_____

Rewrite a nursery rhyme to describe one of the characters in a book you read.

_____

_____

_____

Write a concrete poem about the subject of your book or about one of the characters in it. A concrete poem has a shape that is like the shape of the subject. Arrange the letters, punctuation, and lines to create the right shape.

_____

_____

_____

_____

_____

_____

Operation Decode

Use Morse code or the sign alphabet to tell the title of your book, the author, and a one or two-sentence summary of your book.

Morse Code

A ● ■	B ■ ● ● ●	C ● ● ●	D ■ ● ●
E ●	F ● ● ■ ●	G ■ ■ ●	H ● ● ● ●
I ● ●	J ■ ● ■ ●	K ■ ● ■	L ● ■
M ■ ■	N ■ ●	O ● ●	P ● ● ● ● ●
Q ● ● ● ■ ●	R ● ● ●	S ● ● ●	T ■
U ● ● ■	V ● ● ● ■	W ● ■ ■	X ● ■ ● ●
Y ● ● ● ●	Z ● ● ● ●	& ● ● ● ●	$ ● ● ● ■ ● ●

Numerals

1 ● ■ ■	2 ● ● ■ ● ●	3 ● ● ● ■ ●
4 ● ● ● ● ■	5 ■ ■ ■	6 ● ● ● ● ● ●
7 ■ ■ ● ● ●	8 ■ ● ● ● ●	9 ■ ● ● ● ●
		0 ■

Punctuation

Comma ● ■ ● ■	Period ● ● ■ ● ■ ●	Semicolon ● ● ● ● ●

Interrogation
■ ● ● ■ ●

American Sign Language

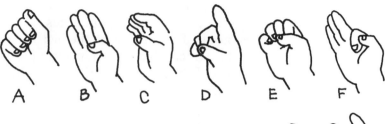

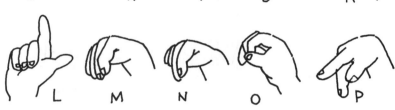
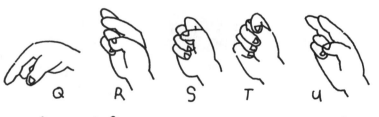

Write your title, author, and brief summary in Morse code on another sheet of paper.

Perform your title, author, and brief summary in sign language for the class. Afterward, *tell* the class what you said in sign language.

Picture This!

Ask students to bring in old magazines and catalogs from home. The library/media center may also have some giveaways. Encourage students to think about a book they have read and carefully select pictures and words that portray or suggest the theme of the book. Distribute large pieces of tagboard to students. Instruct them to fold the tagboard in half to make a "book," and cut out an interesting variety of letters to spell out the author and title on the front cover. Have them decorate the inside of the "book" with an array of pictures, words, or phrases that depict the real book. They may glue the pictures on one side and the words on another, or combine them in a unique, picturesque way. You may wish to stand the collage creations on tables or shelves in the classroom.

Book of the Year!

Think about all the books you have read and enjoyed. Select one as the Book of the Year. Write the title and the author, and draw or copy a scene or character in the space below. Include a short description of the book and a reason for your choice. Your teacher may post the sheets in the classroom or put them in a notebook that may be checked out by classmates.

BOOK OF THE YEAR   BOOK OF THE YEAR   BOOK OF THE YEAR   BOOK OF THE YEAR

BOOK OF THE YEAR

BOOK OF THE YEAR

BOOK OF THE YEAR

BOOK OF THE YEAR

BOOK OF THE YEAR

BOOK OF THE YEAR

BOOK OF THE YEAR   BOOK OF THE YEAR   BOOK OF THE YEAR   BOOK OF THE YEAR

Baseball by the Book

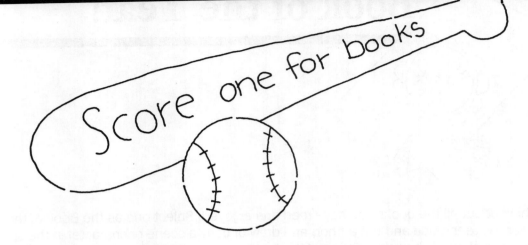

Score one for books

Take the class outside or to the gym for an end-of-the-year activity! Before Game Day, discuss popular books with the class. Ask students to write short questions and answers about books they have read during the year. Have them write each question and answer on a separate index card.

Divide the class into two teams. Set out four pieces of cardboard for the bases. Then read the questions on the cards one by one. If the first student "up to bat" answers a question correctly, he or she goes to first base. If the second player answers correctly, he or she advances to first and the player on first goes to second. Whenever a player reaches home plate, that team scores a point. When a team has three incorrect answers, it is out and the opposing team "goes up to bat." You may play for a specified number of innings or within a certain time limit. Ask the principal or librarian/media specialist to "pitch" the questions while you act as umpire.